For three- to five-year-olds

Grandad's Story

Story by Pie Corbett
Activities by David Bell, Pie Corbett,
Geoff Leyland and Mick Seller

Illustrations by Diann Timms

For Daisy

It was dark and we were tired.
The moon shone on our street.

Have you seen the moon? Was it round?
What do you like doing before you go to bed?
What do you like doing in the morning?
What do you like doing in the afternoon?

Grandad wanted to tell
us a story.

What story do you think he is going to tell?
What are your favourite stories?
Are there any stories you don't like? Why?
What sort of stories do you like?

'Once upon a time there were three tubby bears. . .

Are the children listening to the story?

How do the bears look? Do you think they are kind bears?

What do you think their names are?

. . . who climbed beanstalks
as far as the clouds.

How many plants can you see in the picture? Which are the tallest plants? Which are the smallest?
Are the leaves on each plant the same?
When you next go out look at the different trees and plants. Buy some sunflower seeds and plant them. Follow the instructions on the packet.

At the top they met
three porky pigs.

Look at the pigs' houses.
What are they made of?
Are parts of your house made of wood?
Or of straw? Or of bricks?
Have you seen a house made of wood or
a cottage with a straw roof?

Go outside and look at your own house.
What different materials can you see?
Use your eyes and fingers
and say what each is like.
Is it rough, smooth, hard, soft, shiny?

The porky pigs took the bears through the dark woods to visit their grandmamma.

What different animals can you see in the picture? When you next go for a walk in the woods or the park, look carefully.

How many different kinds of animals can you see?

How many colours of flowers can you see?
Use your nose – how many different smells can you find?

WATCH OUT Don't eat wild berries. Please do not pick any flowers or disturb any animal homes.

But a wolf followed them.
It was thin and hungry.

What do you think the wolf wants to do?
How would you stop him?

What do you think a wolf likes to eat?
What would you give him to eat?

Do you think the wolf will catch the
pigs and bears?

Little Red Riding Hood
saw the wolf and with one loud
clap of her hands
frightened it away.

What would you do to frighten the wolf?
Would you make funny noises?
Or pull funny faces?
Or would you dress up in something frightening?

As it was the end of the story she cuddled the bears. She kissed the pigs . . .

Point to all the pigs you can see.
How many are there?

Point to all the bears.
How many can you see?

How many brown animals are there?

How many animals are wearing blue?

. . . and they turned into frogs.'

All the animals are different sizes.
Who is the tallest bear?
Who is the shortest?
Are any of the bears the same height?
Which frog is the biggest?
And which is the smallest?

What a laugh!
Grandad never gets his
stories right!

What's a good way to start a story?

Can you make up one for someone in your family?

You could do some drawings as well.

We went to wash and clean our teeth.

How do you look after your teeth?

Look in a big mirror.
How many teeth can you see?
Are all the teeth the same
size and shape?

Bite an apple or a chocolate biscuit.
Get a grown-up to do the same.
Compare the teeth marks.

Grandad kissed us goodnight
and turned out the lights.

What did you see the children do when they were in the bathroom? What else do you think they did before they went back to the bedroom?

What did Grandad do first when they were back in the bedroom? What did he do next?

There are many different parts to Grandad's story. How did it begin? How did it end? You could look at the story again if you like.

It was dark and we were tired.

Next time there is a sunny day spend some time looking at shadows.

Try to touch your shadow.
Do you have a shadow in the shade?

Make your shadow small, big, tall, thin, wide.

Can you make your shadow disappear?

Can you make your shadow look like a crocodile, a letter, a number, a tree?

Does everything have a shadow?

Are all shadows the same colour?

The moon shone
on our street.

How many bears can you see? How many pigs can you see?

If one of the bears went away, how many would be left?

If another pig came to play, how many would there be?

Can you see any other animals in the picture?

Count all the animals in the picture.

Activity notes

Pages 2–3 Children need help to understand the passage of time. However, they are able to match different events with specific times of day. For example, getting out of bed, putting on clothes and having breakfast are all associated with morning.
Talk with your child about things that you do together in the afternoon.

Pages 4–5 It's useful to discover what sort of stories your child enjoys so that you can keep your eyes open for more of them. Of course they won't like everything. If they enjoy a series of books or comics then it's worth buying more.
If you were the grandad in the story what tale would you tell?

Pages 6–7 This sort of invitation helps your child to associate with the story. It also helps them read the pictures. Reading the pictures is one step away from reading the words.
Encourage your child to look at the pictures for clues about what is happening.

Pages 8–9 Sorting and grouping are important skills in early science, as well as in maths.
When you're outside, encourage your child to look at how different kinds of flowers are similar, for example, in their colour, their shape, and whether they have a scent.

Pages 10–11 Close observation, using the senses of touch and sight, develops an awareness of the ways in which different materials are used in our environment. Talking about different materials, about what you feel and see, will enlarge your child's vocabulary.

Pages 12–13 This activity encourages careful observation and helps to develop children's understanding of living things: of the way small natural objects are the same or different.
Children enjoy collecting things. When you next go out together see what can be collected, for example, fallen leaves, pine cones, interestingly-shaped or coloured stones, feathers.

Pages 14–15 If your child finds the wolf scary you could help by saying something funny: 'He probably likes jelly much better than little girls! Shall we throw a custard pie at him?'
Try playing 'What's the Time, Mr Wolf'. The players ask the wolf what the time is. The wolf says '1 o'clock', '2 o'clock', etc, then suddenly he says, 'It's time to eat you up' and chases the players.

Pages 16–17 Questions like these help to involve children in the story. Simply listening and chatting with your child helps them feel that the times when you read are warm, happy times. This will encourage a natural love of reading and books.

Pages 18–19 In this activity the children are grouping the animals using different criteria, for example, colour, or type of clothing.
You could try this simple game at home. Group two, three or four objects together and see if your child can guess what criteria you have used to make the set, eg are they all round objects? Are they all green?

Pages 20–21 An understanding of measurement begins with the simple language of comparison such as 'taller than', 'shorter than'. This can easily be introduced into daily life. For example, 'Mummy is taller than you but you are taller than your baby brother'.
Encouraging your child to estimate or guess helps them to develop a feel for measurement.

Pages 22–23 This activity helps to practise story-telling. You could let your child tell you a story and write it down for them. Drawings could be done to go with the story. Another idea is for your child to draw the story in a series of pictures. Pin up the stories and drawings, or make them into a little book.

Pages 24–25 The more children understand about their own bodies, the more independent they will be about looking after themselves.
Talk about what happens to teeth. Do you know a baby who is teething? Or a 'gappy' six-year-old? Does anybody in the family have fillings? How can they be prevented?

Pages 26–27 An understanding of sequence is important in maths, science and English.
Children's stories can help here, as they are often made up of simple, distinct steps. As children become familiar with stories they will learn to predict what is going to happen next.
This is one good reason for encouraging repetition.

Pages 28–29 Investigating shadows is a cornerstone for learning later about the solar system. You could follow up this activity on a sunny day by drawing round your child's shadow. Do it on a pavement or path with chalk. Draw it at the same spot again later in the day and talk about what has happened.
See how many different shadow shapes you can make on the wall.

Pages 30–31 To help your child with simple addition and subtraction, start with a small group of objects. Add or remove one object at a time and ask your child to count how many there are now.
Adding and subtracting becomes more real to children if they can add or remove the objects themselves.